Unified Communications

FOR

DUMMIES®

AVAYA CUSTOM EDITION

by Peter Gregory, CISA, CISSP

BICENTENNIAL
1807
WILEY
2007
BICENTENNIAL

Wiley Publishing, Inc.

Unified Communications For Dummies®, Avaya Custom Edition

Published by
Wiley Publishing, Inc.
111 River Street
Hoboken, NJ 07030-5774

www.wiley.com

WILEY

Publisher's Acknowledgments

We're proud of this book; please send us your comments through our online registration form located at www.dummies.com/register/. For details on how to create a custom *For Dummies* book for your business or organization, contact bizdev@wiley.com. For information about licensing the *For Dummies* brand for products or services, contact BrandedRights&Licenses@Wiley.com.

Some of the people who helped bring this book to market include the following:

Acquisitions, Editorial, and Media Development

Project Editor: Jan Sims

Business Development Representative: Sue Blessing

Editorial Manager: Rev Mengle

Composition Services

Project Coordinator: Kristie Rees

Layout and Graphics: Carl Byers, Julie Trippetti

Proofreader: Jessica Kramer

Anniversary Logo Design: Richard Pacifico

Special Help

Nicole Coppey, Alan Mendelsohn, Diedre Murphy, Jackie Smith

Publishing and Editorial for Technology Dummies

    Richard Swadley, Vice President and Executive Group Publisher

    Andy Cummings, Vice President and Publisher

    Mary Bednarek, Executive Acquisitions Director

    Mary C. Corder, Editorial Director

Publishing for Consumer Dummies

    Diane Graves Steele, Vice President and Publisher

    Joyce Pepple, Acquisitions Director

Composition Services

    Gerry Fahey, Vice President of Production Services

    Debbie Stailey, Director of Composition Services

Table of Contents

Introduction

· ·

*W*hen it comes to employee effectiveness and communications, many organizations are simply floundering in a sea of options for person-to-person communications. Almost without exception, none of these options are integrated with any other, and most are like a message in a bottle: You have to try and contact someone, without knowing their availability, ability, or willingness to participate or respond.

It is taking more and more time for workers (and customers and business associates) to get in touch with other workers because they need to try one method after another, each time looking up different contact information, and each time not knowing whether the recipient is even "on the air."

Unified Communications aims to transform all of this chaos.

About This Book

This book introduces you to the many advantages a Unified Communications strategy can bring to any business, and explains a bit of the technology that helps you get there.

Unified Communications brings together communications standards and protocols that can bind these now-disparate communications channels so that they become aware of each other and a lot easier to use. This approach can dramatically improve worker effectiveness as well as enhance customer satisfaction.

Employee effectiveness is improved because each attempt at communications has a far better chance of reaching the right person at the right time using the optimal medium. With Unified Communications, the originator (from whatever mode of communication he or she chooses) can tell in advance whether the recipient is willing and able to communicate and what his or her preferred mode is at that moment.

Customer satisfaction is enhanced because call center reps, helpdesk techs, and account reps have an easier time finding subject-matter-experts within the organization, increasing the likelihood of first-call resolution. Further, when customers themselves desire to communicate with someone in the organization, Unified Communications can make a live contact far more likely, regardless of where that person is working.

How This Book Is Organized

The main purpose of this book is to help you understand Unified Communications — its makeup and business benefits. Ultimately, it shows how you can create a Unified Communications strategy for your own organization. This book is organized into five parts, but you don't have to read them in order — feel free to jump in where it looks most relevant to your current business needs.

Chapter 1: New Working Paradigms

In Chapter 1, I describe how today's myriad communications capabilities often make it difficult and time-consuming for workers to find each other and get the answers they need now. I include several examples of scenarios where a unified solution can come to the rescue.

Chapter 2: Meeting Business Needs with Emerging Communications

Chapter 2 explores the universe of Unified Communications capabilities, and how they improve worker and business effectiveness. I discuss specific benefits for different types of workers and again provide examples of several business scenarios saved by unified solutions.

Chapter 3: Establishing a Unified Communications Strategy

Unified Communications may be grand, but how are you going to get there? In Chapter 3 I take you step by step through the development of a Unified Communications strategy, helping you focus on issues, costs, and business outcomes. I also provide some real-life examples of champion unified strategies that worked.

Chapter 4: Evolving into Intelligent Communications

In Chapter 4, I explain where all this unifying of your communications can take you: all the way to the brilliant promise of Intelligent Communications. Intelligent Communications is the goal beyond the goal that makes Unified Communications worth every penny as your company prepares to meet the future with a real competitive edge.

Chapter 5: Eight Tips for Implementing Unified Communications

Chapter 5, in the celebrated *For Dummies* listing style, highlights eight great ideas that can help you develop and implement your Unified Communications strategy.

Conventions Used in This Book

Icons are used throughout this book to call attention to material worth noting in a special way. Here is a list of the icons along with a description of each:

If you see a Tip icon, pay attention — you're about to find out how to save some aggravation, time or money.

This icon indicates technical information that is probably most interesting to IT professionals.

Some points bear repeating, and others bear remembering. When you see this icon, take special note of what you're about to read.

Look for Warning icons to identify potential pitfalls, including easily confused or difficult-to-understand terms and concepts.

Often in this book, I abbreviate Unified Communications as *UC.* It takes less space, reads faster, and means I can pack even more information about UC into this book.

Where to Go from Here

It's easier to start down the Unified Communications path in your organization than you may think. Much of your existing technology can be re-used or re-purposed; you can develop a roadmap to bring UC into your organization at a pace that's appropriate for your needs, and in a sequence that helps you to address your most critical needs first.

Regardless of where you are in your UC plan, keep your eye on the big picture: UC will enhance not just efficiency but also effectiveness in your organization. Avaya is the UC expert with strategic vision and leadership in UC, converged networks, and security. Companies that go with Avaya enjoy all of the benefits of Avaya's knowledge and experience. Discover for yourself why Avaya is the undisputed leader in delivering business-enabling communications solutions for all-sized businesses.

Chapter 1

New Working Paradigms

● ●

In This Chapter

▶ Understanding the state of communications technology today

▶ Exploring the facets of mobile communications

▶ Satisfying customer expectations

▶ Understanding where to go from here

● ●

A paradigm shift invokes a new way of looking at an old problem, and that is what companies have to deal with in facing the age-old challenge of internal and external communications. Companies need a shift in perspective from focusing on solving microtasks with special features on end-user devices and applications to simplifying communications overall and ensuring that people can initiate, receive, and conduct communications when, where, how, and with whomever they please without having to learn a lot of complicated new technologies. By integrating communications across the broad spectrum of modes, applications, and devices, all systems become more human-friendly.

This book explores new paradigms for working and communicating efficiently and collaboratively. Beyond PCs, Web portals, office phones, smartphones and mobile devices lies the promised land of Unified Communications. It's closer than you may have imagined.

Unified Communications is an evolving approach to communications that solves countless issues in the modern, mobile work environment, or, more accurately, wherever you're doing business these days. This chapter describes the current communications glitches and hitches that drain companies of valuable productive time and resources. It also demonstrates how a Unified Communications strategy begins to transform these splintered technologies into a coherent solution.

Coping with Splintered Communications

Workers today have many means for communications. Companies provide the basics: office phone, voicemail, FAX, e-mail, and sometimes instant messaging, meet-me audio conferencing, and now Web and video conferencing.

Individually, each mode of communicating works well for some needs, but overall these have proven inadequate for many purposes. E-mail is certainly quicker than an old-fashioned letter, so people typically have high expectations for e-mail responsiveness, but often it falls short. People are inundated with too many e-mail messages, and just because you sent an e-mail to someone it does not release you of the responsibility of achieving a business objective. Also, people aren't glued to their office chairs, or are busy on calls all day long, so phone calling is less than optimal for a fast answer. At least there's voice-mail, but who knows when the recipient will listen — and respond — to messages?

To fill certain gaps in communication needs, office workers have started using new technologies on their own (regardless of whether the IT department supports them), such as:

- **Mobile/cell phones:** With a penetration rate of over 50 percent, it's easy to say now that most office workers have cell phones. Many put their cell phone numbers on their business cards. Cell phones come with their own voice-mail capability, separate from office voice-mail.

- **Smartphones and PDAs:** The capabilities on mobile phones and PDAs are converging, creating a new generation of smartphones that are capable of accessing the Internet, sending and receiving e-mail, maintaining calendars and contact lists, and storing and using company information. Workers often purchase one of these convenient gadgets for both personal and business use.

- **Text messaging:** Mobile phone users can send text messages to each other. The major mobility carriers also gateway text messaging with each other and with Internet e-mail.

✔ **Instant messaging:** For those who think e-mail is not instantaneous enough, and when an enterprise has not deployed enterprise-wide IM from software vendors (such as Microsoft, IBM, Jabber), employees are enrolling on their own service (such as MSN, Yahoo, Google, AOL, and Skype). Some of these IM solutions now permit Internet-based phone conversations and even gateway services so that IM users can make phone calls to land-lines and mobile users, and vice-versa.

✔ **Personal e-mail:** Most office workers also have personal e-mail accounts, with such services as AOL, Yahoo, Gmail, Hotmail, MSN, and many others. Although many workers keep a more-or-less clean separation between business and personal use, sometimes they may resort to using personal e-mail for business purposes when their company-provided e-mail is unavailable or inconvenient.

✔ **Internet-based FAX:** There are several free and fee-based Internet-oriented FAX services, wherein an incoming fax can be directed to a user's e-mail, and users can originate faxes from their e-mail.

Today's workers, then, have many means for communicating with each other and with customers, partners, and suppliers: office phone, meet-me conferencing, office voicemail, e-mail, FAX, mobile phone, mobile phone voicemail, Internet FAX, instant messaging, text messaging, notification services, TTY, in-building wireless solutions, and Internet phone calls, not to mention high-end options such as Video and Web conferencing.

On the surface, it may seem as if companies with such a vast array of options are living in a communications nirvana, but exactly the opposite is true. With all of these means available for communications, workers now have many more ways to communicate, all inconsistent with one another, thereby ironi-cally increasing the odds of missing the person you want to reach.

Recognizing risks and counterproductivity

In the "old days", you called someone, sent them an e-mail, and perhaps called his mobile phone. If you could not get through, you left messages and waited. Sometimes, you left a message in all three modes to advise of the original message left in a different mode. Today, you have many other means available for attempting communications, often wasting time looking up cell phone, IM, text messaging, and other e-mail addresses, with no certainty that your communications will reach the intended recipient. Some issues that arise are:

- **Costs of managing and maintaining disparate networks, applications, and devices can be high for IT departments, not to mention time-consuming.** Trying to keep all employees' communications devices simply up to speed with the latest apps and updates and security patches can keep IT staff busy days, nights, and weekends.

- **Communications channels unaware of each other.** Nearly every means available for communications exists as an island and is unaware of other available means. You usually have to try several channels before you make a connection; indeed, if you don't try them all, you risk not getting connected or your message being overlooked as not that important.

- **Multiple directories in use with partial information stored in each.** With so many different means for communication, a user may not have access to the "right" directory, or the directory that they have may not have the "right" connection options or information — no company directory or single device can possibly track all of the various means, phone numbers, and addresses for company workers. Often the only way that workers know about these covert channels is on their own "buddy lists" or personal contact lists, which by their nature are private and not shared.

- **Private communication for official business.** When folks start trying to reach workers by means not provided by the business (mobile phone, consumer IM, Internet FAX), you risk having communications between customers, partners, suppliers and office workers that take place on popular "public" channels that the company doesn't govern. The business is now no longer aware of such communications and so it cannot track, control or report on them.

- **Risk of disclosure.** Most of these "public" means for communications have less protection than businesses require: Most IM services are unencrypted, personal e-mail is unencrypted and stored on multi-tenant servers, and Internet-based FAX is as unprotected as e-mail. Business information, therefore, exists on many service providers' systems, away from corporate control and protection, putting the business at risk of noncompliance with data protection and retention regulations and policies.

- ✔ **Undocumented communications.** Businesses are under increasing requirements to document their internal communications as well as communications with outside parties such as customers and suppliers. When communications take place over means not controlled by the business, the business is unable to archive such communications, putting it at risk of regulatory noncompliance.

Choosing not to continue like this

The morass of communications choices, both business-owned and not-business-owned, are creating efficiency and regulatory problems. Companies of all sizes are in desperate need of some means for all of these isolated means for communications to somehow be knitted together so that they can act more as a unified whole and not like the splintered services they are today.

Unified Communications pulls it all together again by integrating various modes of communication so they can work together seamlessly for the end users. When done well, Unified Communications changes everyone's expectations: Instead of communications being fragmented and frustrating, they become a cohesive whole.

New Business Communications Realities

The entire communications landscape has changed. Mobility is firmly established and becoming more feature-rich and versatile. More employees work in diverse locations and use a wider range of communications options. I explore these developments in this section.

Staying connected on the racing circuit

Honda's Formula 1 racing team, based in the U.K., consists of over 70 employees who are on the road eight months out of the year. The team packs up and moves from location to location throughout the world every two weeks, and must be fully connected upon arrival at the next race site.

The team's IT department must contend with local laws, telephone companies, and tight installation schedules for local ISDN lines. Every two weeks, every team member is assigned a new landline number (they have cellular phones also, but that also proves a challenge when operating on every continent in the world).

Honda's campus was growing and had disparate phone systems that could not talk with each other. They were unable to transfer calls, and calls between employees in different buildings had to go through the local exchange.

Honda turned to Avaya for relief from their growing communications challenge, and Avaya provided an IP solution that solved the capacity problem and much more. By implementing Avaya Communications Applications with Communication Manager software in combination with Avaya IP Telephones and Avaya IP Softphone software, the results were stunning:

- Increased collaboration among employees

- Faster, more productive linkage of mobile workers with headquarters experts

- More effective communications with suppliers

- Reduced IT maintenance

- Easier collaboration among remote teams: all remote team members are reachable, regardless of their location in the world, through their permanent extension number.

- Cost savings exceeding 30 percent

For a real checkered-flag finish, Avaya delivered results within the narrow window between the racing season and winter racing trials: just two weeks!

Multimodal workers' blended connectivity

Company workers are scattered all over: The model of cubicle workers plus an outside sales force is changing. Many traditional office workers are going virtual. Here is an example:

This is nothing less than a revolution in one of the basic tenets of corporate culture: where people work.

Through the 1990s, businesses did a good job of building campus communications infrastructures for their workers, nearly all of whom were located in the office. Now workers have to be able to communicate when they are roaming the campus environment and away from their desks, and workers are scattering to the four winds and working at home, customer locations, hotel rooms, and in coffee shops — anywhere that broadband communications can go.

This mobility creates a challenge that is bigger than just extending the corporate voice and data network over the Internet to virtual workers' locations: It demands a richer communications experience that acts as a partial substitute for not being in the corporate cube farm. Technologies such as video communications and video conferencing are more critical than before.

Virtual workers are also more likely to have a greater diversity of terminal types than before. The proliferation of smartphones and PDAs adds potential complication to the delivery of rich communications services. All of these changes are compelling companies to begin considering a Unified Communications strategy.

Mobility is here to stay

At the same time workers are working more out-of-office, mobility communications services are still enjoying a high rate of growth. Mobility service providers are producing services that operate at higher bandwidth, using handsets that resemble micro-laptops with Web browsers, e-mail, and even document and spreadsheet programs. Prices are dropping, bringing these services into reach of an expanding market. The global mobile workforce is expected to grow by more than 20 percent in the next four years, with 878 million mobile workers toiling away on laptops, handhelds and cell phones by 2009, according to a recent study by IDC (www.idc.com).

Law firm represents a good case for Unified Communications

Sutherland Asbill & Brennan LLP is one of those big law firms known for solving challenging business problems and resolving unique legal issues for many of the nation's largest companies. Founded in 1924, Sutherland has grown to more than 425 lawyers in Atlanta, Austin, Houston, New York, Tallahassee, and Washington, D.C. Sutherland's main practices include corporate, energy, intellectual property, litigation, real estate, and tax.

For Sutherland, business-as-usual extends beyond locations and business hours. Its attorneys needed to take advantage of mobile devices to securely access desktop e-mail regardless of time or location. Their phone system was comprised of six independent, separate telephone systems, each with its own feature set and codes. As a result, the firm did not have the ability to broadcast company-wide voicemail, forward live calls between offices, or deploy one standard feature set for its more than 2,700 telephones.

Being responsive to their clients' needs was extraordinarily difficult, until they implemented Avaya solutions.

The Sutherland IT department began an assessment of its current IT and telephony architecture. The firm knew that the right replacement solution would need to address interoperability, mobility, business continuity, and simpler administration. A good starting point was the creation of an enterprise-wide system that could interoperate with existing technology, including Cisco data infrastructure and Microsoft Exchange.

Sutherland worked with an Avaya Business Partner to systematically replace the separate phone systems at each office with Avaya Media Servers and Avaya Media Gateways and take advantage of technologies such as Avaya Extension to Cellular and Modular Messaging.

The results exceeded Sutherland's expectations:

✔ **Increased mobility.** Sutherland attorneys can now conduct business whenever — and wherever — necessary. Sutherland attorneys are taking advantage of Avaya *Extension to Cellular*, a feature of Avaya Communication Manager that transparently bridges calls to cellular telephones, regardless of location or wireless service provider. Users on cell phones can easily transfer calls, conference with other parties, and toggle between multiple calls, helping to improve productivity and client service while outside the office.

✔ **Increased productivity.** With its Avaya solution in place, Sutherland has gained new levels of productivity, extending value to the firm's clients. Now attorneys are easier to reach and transactions are easier to conduct from any location. Using Avaya Modular Messaging with Microsoft Exchange Server, attorneys stay productive with one business phone number, one message mailbox, and a single directory of client contact information.

✔ **Operational efficiency.** The firm gains a robust infrastructure to unify its offices for greater operational efficiency and manageability. IT has the added capability of simplified statistical reporting.

Before switching to Avaya, securing and compiling regulatory reports or productivity information was labor-intensive or not always possible. Systems now integrated with Avaya telephony architecture, allow secure storage and retrieval for the 7.5 million messages arriving at Sutherland and the 1.5 million searchable documents critical to the firm.

✔ **Superior business continuity.** Avaya Communication Manager delivers high performance and disaster recovery by providing centralized control and alternate routing across the firm's distributed network of gateways and communication devices.

People are showing up at work with personally-owned Blackberries, Treos, Blackjacks, Q's, iPaqs, Sidekicks, UTStarcoms, and many others. These devices offer many mobile computing capabilities including:

- ✔ E-mail
- ✔ Smartphone/IP phone
- ✔ Calendaring and contact management
- ✔ Document reading/editing
- ✔ Internet access
- ✔ IM/SMS

On the surface this trend would appear to be a boon to office productivity, but there are several downsides to these devices as well, including

✔ **Lack of central management.** Few, if any, means are available for an organization to be even aware of such devices, much less to have any ability to support or manage them.

✔ **Risk of information disclosure.** Mobile devices are easily lost or misplaced and often stolen. They provide less protection for their contents than are available for laptops and other "traditional" mobile devices. And when these devices are not owned by the organization, the business is implicitly permitting its confidential information to be stored on systems it does not own or control.

This situation leads to higher support costs and frustrated users, who must take more effort to manage their devices and their communications. These users are not communicating effectively, and the organization is largely unable to help them.

Many networks, one cloud

No single communication mode, from text to video, can replace all the others. Each fulfills a useful function and may be the right solution in different given circumstances. Moreover, workers aren't willing to give up any of them, and sometimes use more than one of these methods at once. Yet using so many devices can be cumbersome for the worker, coworkers, customers, and IT: Each mode has its separate way of addressing users; each has its separate methods of creating and managing contact lists; each has its separate ways of establishing communications sessions. Each may have its own separate devices for doing the communicating.

Executives, employees, customers, and partners alike want all of these various and sundry networks to work together, somehow. You want them to be aware of each other. You want one way of addressing users. You want a single contact list, used for all modes, reachable on all of your applications, terminals, and devices. You want fewer devices to carry around to stay in touch and on top of things. Although you communicate with coworkers and customers over many networks, you want it to act like one "cloud" in the corporate communications diagram.

What you want is Unified Communications.

Satisfying Customer Expectations

After decades of cost-cutting and eroding customer service, consumers and corporate customers have had it with "automated" solutions. They feel like rats in a maze in poorly designed phone-based menuing systems with the inability to talk with a real person.

Catering to customer preferences for contact

Companies have remained focused on customer service as the forefront of business image and reputation.

But while companies have been getting the automated customer service problem under control, at the same time the trends of mobility, splintered communications, and virtual workers have undercut the progress by making it more difficult to find and communicate with employees. Sometimes it feels like two steps forward, one step back. That's why Avaya takes unifying communications a few steps further.

Improving customer interactions

Improving customer expectations means ensuring positive interactions with them. Here are some ways that more integrated communications can make your company stand out from the crowd:

✔ **Simplify interactions with customers**. A single "phone" number can be used to access an associate for a variety of services be it voice, fax, notification, or TTY; at any location be it at their office desk, around the office, on their mobile device, virtual or work-at-home office, or on their PC from anywhere in the world. Now you can find out quickly who's available to answer a customer's question or solve a vendor's problem, and if you catch the call just coming back from lunch, the customer need never know: A call that was started on a desk phone can be transferred to a cell phone, or from cell phone to desk phone without interruption while the call is in progress.

✔ **Increase availability of associates**. Simultaneous ringing of business line and cell phone and find-me/follow-me services increases the probability that a caller can reach the intended person on the first attempt.

✔ **Increase responsiveness**. Employees can be reached or initiate real-time and non-real-time communications from anywhere. They have increased access to other associates to deal with customer issues. All business voice messages are managed in a single mailbox eliminating the challenge of how to forward an important message that is left in a mailbox associated with a cell phone to another associate for information or action. Improved notification of- and access to messages (e-mail, voicemail, or fax), and increased ability to manage those messages accelerates the ability to deal with customer demands.

Establishing Unified Communications

Unified Communications, which I'll also call UC for short in the rest of the book, is a major step in the direction organizations need to take. UC simplifies your communications by logically blending and combining previously separate services and features so that communications by any means with anyone is possible over any of your devices.

In the remainder of this book, I show you how you can establish a strategy for UC in your organization. In Chapter 2, I discuss in detail the features available in Unified Communications and how they permit new capabilities that drive customer satisfaction and make your processes and communications more effective.

In Chapter 3, I take you through the specific steps needed to establish a UC strategy in your organization — to take you from where you are now through a revolution in communications effectiveness that will make your organization stronger, while enabling your employees and your customers to manage and use your products and services more effectively.

Then, in Chapter 4, I show you what lies beyond the horizon: Intelligent Communications. Your UC strategy can take you down the path into Intelligent Communications where customer satisfaction continues to improve while communications costs are further reduced.

Chapter 2

Meeting Business Needs with Emerging Communications

*Y*ou may think that the plethora of communications choices is a boon for business. You may be surprised, then, to find out that businesses are actually suffering under the load of so many communications channels. Primarily this overload is because all of these communications technologies are largely unaware of one another. So instead of getting one message on your voicemail, you receive a voicemail, an e-mail, and an IM from one person trying to reach you at the office . . . when you had your cell phone with you all along.

This communication overload is exacerbated by today's increasingly-mobile workforce. Workers don't all sit in cubicles and offices any more — at least not every day. More and more workers are going "virtual" — working at home, while traveling, in coffee shops, or wherever. This mobility has made it more time-consuming than ever to communicate with coworkers, because we don't know the best way to reach them at any given time.

There is plenty of reason to have hope: UC is a set of emerging technologies that can unify today's disparate methods of communications into a set of multimodal capabilities that are highly aware of one another. This means that it will be easier to reach people — and to let others know how to reach you — than ever before. Avaya is leading the way here, by developing communications technologies and products to make communications more effective and meaningful.

In this chapter I take you on a deep dive into UC, from the perspectives of technology as well as business effectiveness.

Exploring Unified Communications Technologies

UC represents the ongoing advancement in many communications technologies. But unlike the independent advancement of these technologies in the past, with UC these technologies are aware of each other and take advantage of each other's capabilities. The boundaries between the once-separate modes of communications are blurring, both technically and functionally. There's always some overlap between some of these technologies' capabilities, and that's no accident. In fact, it's a part of the deliberate convergence of communications technologies.

Telephony

Ever since Alexander Graham Bell's first telephonic words, "Mr. Watson—Come here—I want to see you!", the technology supporting telephony has been steadily advancing. With the advent of UC, Bell can reach Watson anywhere, anytime, so Watson doesn't even need to "come here."

In UC, telephony takes on new forms, including

- **UC clients:** Thick or thin, built into PCs or traditional-*looking* telephones, UC clients communicate with each other directly or through IP PBXs using Voice over IP (VoIP) technology.

- **IP Phone Applications:** Because you can access and control your voice communications from your PC, why not access your computer information from your phone? With IP Phone Applications, your office phone can be turned into a PDA with access to e-mail, calendar, contacts, and tasks. The next time you arrive late at the office and need to dial into a meeting — the logistics of which are in your calendar or buried deep in an e-mail — you can turn to that "always on" device sitting on your desk — the phone — and access the information that you require while your PC is still booting up.

✓ **Embedded Communications:** While using applications such as e-mail, instant messaging, or perhaps while accessing files from a collaboration site, users can confirm presence and availability, and if desired initiate a communication via e-mail, IM, or phone call without needing to switch to a different application.

✓ **UC-enabled SIP phones:** A variation of UC clients, SIP phones use the popular Session Initiation Protocol that supports a variety of communication modes such as voice, conferencing, and instant messaging.

✓ **Audio-video phones:** UC clients and phones can support not only audio, but also video communications. Users will start saying, "Can you see me now? Good!"

✓ **Dual-mode wireless phones:** Switching automatically between local WiFi and regional CDMA or GSM, new mobile phones will connect to corporate WiFi voice networks when on-campus, and to telcos' cellular networks otherwise.

UC ties together all of the different types of voice communications that are available today.

New contact methods

The bane of communications today is not their variety, but their separateness, especially when it comes to attempts to raise a communication channel with your friend or colleague. With UC, your contact identities collapse into fewer identities.

Today you likely have separate numbers for desk, mobile, fax, virtual office, voicemail, TTY, pager, and so on. In UC, these merge into

✓ **Single Number Access:** Whether you want to talk live, leave voicemail, request a notification, send a fax, or communicate via TTY, you access a single number. The network and the endpoints figure out how to match available technologies to get the message (or the voice call) through.

✔ **Single Outbound Identity:** The reverse of Single Number Access, Single Outbound Identity shows a single "calling" number, regardless of the mode of communications used. A recipient can recognize your single number, no matter what technology you're using to communicate.

This new model heralds the return of easily navigated business cards — imagine a business card with one number for everything!

Call coverage

When someone calls you, do you want the call to be routed to your assistant, your voicemail, or some other destination? Does it depend on who's calling? Call coverage in UC permits the user to set up simple rules that direct incoming calls straight to voicemail, a live assistant, a call center, or almost anyplace else.

An incoming call can also be routed to a speech assistant that can ask questions and record answers, and make decisions on-the-fly about how to handle the call.

Workstation-telephony integration

UC communications are easily integrated with existing desktop and laptop based computing environments. Some of the features that users will enjoy are:

Desktop telephony, the ability to use your PC with a thick or Web-based software client, enables you to control your business extension. As Figure 2-1 shows, regardless of where you're working from, you can place and receive calls, manage calls in progress, and use advanced telephony features, all while maintaining your business extension identity. The end-user experience is the same for all three of these modes, all of which Avaya supports:

✔ **Shared:** A PC thick or Web-based client and regular office phone share the call control features, while the voice path is directed to the office phone. A call that you answer or initiate using the client software or the office desk phone can be managed with the other. You can answer a call using the telephone, then place the call on hold using your PC. Then you can retrieve the call from hold and forward the call using the buttons on the phone.

✓ **PC only:** A PC thick or Web-based client provides exclusive call control while the PC, using VoIP, carries the voice aspect of the call.

✓ **Any phone:** A PC thick or Web-based client provides exclusive call control while the voice is sent to a user-designated telephone. Inbound calls ring at the designated telephone; outbound calls first call the user at the designated number and then place the outbound portion of the call.

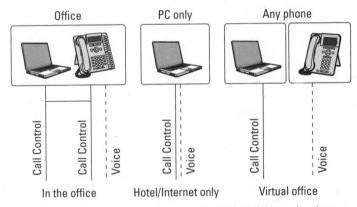

Office   PC only   Any phone

Call Control   Call Control   Voice   Call Control   Voice   Call Control   Voice

In the office   Hotel/Internet only   Virtual office

Figure 2-1: Maintaining your enterprise identity for all inbound and outbound calls.

Mobility

Mobility is all about cutting the cord tying you to your desk and going where you want to. UC brings even more capabilities to mobility, including

✓ **Multiband and dual-/tri-mode phones:** Sure, you've seen phones with CDMA, GSM, and AMPS, but that's yesterday's news. What's coming with UC are phones that can switch seamlessly from corporate WiFi networks to mobility networks and back again.

✔ **Mobile UC clients:** A consistent seamless experience is one of the goals of UC. The use of a mobile client enables you to visually manage your e-mail and voice messages, access the corporate directory, and extend corporate PBX features such as transfer, conference, and others to your mobile device.

✔ **Text-to-speech:** When considering unified messaging, you may first think of the ability to manage your voice messages from your e-mail client. You can also have your e-mail messages read to you while you're accessing your voice messages. In some cases, you can even have the attachment read to you.

✔ **Speech recognition:** Sometimes it's inconvenient or inappropriate to use a device to manage your communications. Speech recognition is ideally suited for mobile use. It provides eyes-free, hands-free, speaker-independent access to calling and conferencing, e-mail and voicemail, calendar, and task lists.

Today's cell phones have the necessary hardware for these capabilities; only the software and standards are missing. Avaya's innovation in mobility brings new life and capabilities into mobile communications.

Messaging and notification

Today's messaging can seem quite fragmented as you try to find out whether the person you want to message with has a compatible provider. Consider today's separate islands of messaging:

✔ **Voicemail:** With separate voicemail boxes — home office voicemail, mobile voicemail, and desk phone voicemail — the voicemail systems are islands, so you lose the utility of the message. In other words, you can't transfer, forward, or reply because you're using disparate systems and directories.

✔ **Instant messaging:** Today you have no interoperability between the major instant messaging (IM) providers such as MSN IM, AOL IM, Google Talk, or Skype. In fact, integration between these services and enterprise IM is also scant. A few client programs communicate with two or more of these applications but there are few gateway capabilities out there.

Now, imagine a communications scenario where, instead of these messaging networks being isolated, they're all interconnected, providing capabilities such as

- **Single voicemail:** Instead of having to check voicemail on the office phone, mobile phone, and possibly other places, workers have a single voicemail system that they can access anywhere. Voicemail indicators signal both office *and* mobile phones, as well as desktop applications.

- **Cross-media reply:** Instead of separate messaging infrastructures for e-mail, voicemail, and text messages, a single infrastructure supports messaging and replies in various media, including

  - Voicemail responses to e-mail.

  - E-mail or text responses to voicemail.

- **Federated instant messaging:** Instead of separate islands of proprietary and private instant messaging systems, UC makes possible instant messaging environments between organizations and carriers that permit people to reach others via instant messaging, regardless of the IM service that each is using.

- **Click to call, click to conference:** Messages, directories, and contact lists empower a user to immediately call or conference with others on whatever media is available at the time.

- **Unified messaging:** You get e-mail, voicemail, and fax in a single inbox.

- **Visual voicemail on all devices, including mobile:** Sort, scan, select specific messages so you can focus on what is important. Just as you can "see" e-mail on your Blackberry, now you can get voicemail that way, too.

- **Notification:** The Avaya Event Processor has built-in components for scanning databases, RSS feeds, and other event sources to keep you in the loop in real time, and the Avaya Communications Process Manager has built-in modules for orchestrating responses to events, without human-introduced latency. Avaya Modular Messaging and one-X Speech provide a number of notification services with user-controlled Call-me rules that can make connections to scheduled events automated. For example, a caller can request that a notification message be sent with their call-back information. Also, one-X Speech can outcall to remind you of tasks, appointments, and meetings. Together, these solutions enable much faster organizational responsiveness.

UC *unifies* today's disparate communications environments into single-pipeline, multimedia networks that permit people to reach each other — and share all kinds of data — with whatever communication technology they happen to have at hand.

Conferencing

Audio, Web, and video conferencing takes on new capabilities with UC. Some of the features that UC brings to conferencing are:

- ✔ **Device independence:** Participants can join a conference via any of these devices: audio-only mobile phone, UC smartphone, PDA, or PC Web portal.

- ✔ **Conference call-out:** The conferencing system calls out to the meeting host and participants instead of having everyone dial IN. Meetings can get started more promptly. No searching for dial-in numbers: Just answer the phone when it rings.

- ✔ **Media adaptability:** A conference that starts in one mode can easily and quickly add other modes. For example, an audio conference can easily add a video clip or stream, images, application sharing, and so on, right in the conference, without any adjustments required.

- ✔ **Integrated scheduling:** When someone organizes a conference, invited participants' calendars are automatically updated. The organizer can, with the "push of a button" (okay, typing a URL in a browser), have conference information automatically added to an invite, so that its participants won't have to figure out how to join the conference at the appointed time.

- ✔ **Visual audio conference control:** Conference organizers can — in real time — control video and audio aspects of the conference. This enables a media-rich conference to be smarter about participants' capabilities. Participants with rich media capabilities can see the video, the audio, the application sharing, and so on, if their terminals are capable, while participants on lighter terminals such as mobile devices can receive the parts of the conference that their devices enable.

PIM: Syncing calendars, contacts, and so on

Trying to manage the multiple contact lists and calendars in your applications can become frustrating enough that you give up. In many cases, you have no means for synchronizing calendars and contact lists between various applications. And even where there *are* tools available for synchronizing, they can be difficult to use and problematic.

Movin' on down with unified transportation

Trucking companies have historically had a difficult time answering the age-old questions: "Where is my shipment?" and "Why is my shipment late?"

Processes related to trucking logistics and exception processing are often inefficient, and they lack adequate information, which results in the inability to reset customer expectations or intervene in the source of the delay itself.

UC can aid trucking companies to overcome these inefficiencies by providing several points of communication and automation, including:

✔ Text and voice messaging to each vehicle and driver

✔ GPS location technology for each vehicle

✔ Telemetry data that aids the driver and central dispatch on specific issues and events related to the condition and performance of the vehicle

These solutions can provide better and up-to-date information for dispatch, which can intervene more quickly and appropriately with replacement drivers, field vehicle repairs, towing, and replacement vehicles. The business results realized from these actions include:

✔ Decreased delays in delivery schedules

✔ Better utilization of fleet resources

✔ Improved customer service

✔ More repeat business and references from satisfied customers

You guessed it — UC makes this arduous task easier than before. Seamless and elegant, UC makes contact and calendar management as though you have only one calendar and contact list that you are accessing through many means.

Presence and availability

With UC, you still have and use many modes of communication: mobile phone, desk phone, instant messaging, video conferencing, e-mail, and more. Yet UC solves two primary problems:

- ✔ **Presence** helps you determine, *in advance*, how another colleague can most easily and expeditiously be contacted.

- ✔ **Availability** helps you indicate how a colleague can contact you, including what sorts of incoming contacts you prefer.

Here is how these UC features work.

When a user activates his or her communications device, it registers its presence on the network, indicating its ability to communicate. Presence distributes the following information to other network users (including those who wish to communicate with another):

- ✔ **User presence:** Whether the person is online or offline, in the office or on the road, active in a sharing application or idle, and so on (also, can express presence with messages such as: in a meeting, on the phone, or out to lunch). An early manifestation of presence is the IM buddy list that shows whether your contacts are online or offline.

- ✔ **User capability:** What modes of communication the person can receive. For example, you may know that someone is capable of receiving a video call instead of just a plain old voice call.

- ✔ **User availability:** Whether the person is willing to participate in communications at that time with you. Probably the earliest manifestation of availability is the telephone network's "busy signal", signaling to a caller that the party is unable to communicate right now because he or she is already communicating with someone else.

Healthier unified patient scheduling

Health care service delivery is all about people: Medical staff support each other and provide services to patients. Secondarily, the right equipment must be available when and where needed.

Having adopted just-in-time service delivery to patients and support staff, today's medical practices, clinics, and hospitals are stretched to the limit when providing medical services to patients. Financial pressures have taken all of the slack out of the delivery system. This makes efficient patient scheduling a critical element in the delivery of services.

Health care delivery schedules are priority-driven and subject to disruptive emergencies that take away critical personnel and resources at the last minute, resulting in delays and the inability to accurately reschedule services. Delays and glitches in scheduling may result in:

✔ Lost revenue for medical service providers

✔ Reduced productivity

✔ Inefficient use of scarce resources

✔ Poor patient satisfaction

UC can provide information about the availability of providers, resources, and patients. Some of the capabilities that can be brought to bear on this problem include:

✔ Communications-enabled resource scheduling processes that provide real-time resource availability

✔ Real-time notification to personnel when resources will be delayed due to last-minute emergencies

✔ Real-time notification to patients when service delays are likely, including updates on rescheduling

Such capabilities can result in fewer surprises, happier patients, and greater efficiencies.

You can also typically tell the system (though there's no need for the system to broadcast it to those who want to reach you) your preferred method of contact — whether you want to receive communications via IM, desk phone, cell phone, and so on. The convenience of UC is that even when someone calls you on your desk phone, you can have your cell phone ring if that's what you've designated as your contact preference at that moment.

Presence and availability are partly about status, and partly about preference. Just because you *can* communicate doesn't mean you *want* to. Typically, you need to be available all the time to your manager, no matter what else you're doing, but you can be more selective about who else you accept calls and messages from at different times or under various circumstances.

Finally, these capabilities are not just about a recipient managing his or her preference for being interrupted. There is a much loftier goal: ensuring that the right people are known and reachable in any given circumstance.

Putting Technologies Together

UC isn't about piling on newfangled technology solely because of its coolness factor. Rather, UC is about the fulfillment of important *business objectives* through the use of specific technologies. (That said, you'll still find many of the technologies brought to bear on specific business challenges are way-cool.)

Personal and team effectiveness

Effectiveness means *getting the right things done*. Talk with nearly anyone about a given big project or initiative and ask what the most important success (or failure) factors were, and most of the time *communications* are near the top of the list. UC is about making your communications more effective so that both you and whatever teams you work with get more significant tasks done instead of frittering time on insignificant ones.

Some examples of effectiveness include:

- ✔ **Directing and prioritizing interaction:** Understanding the norms for communicating greatly improves outcomes when everyone knows how (both in terms of *means* and *style*) the team can best communicate.

- ✔ **Improving response efficiency:** Persons and groups can respond more quickly, keeping tasks and projects on-time, if they are easier to reach. A person who isn't reachable isn't able to respond.

✔ **Improving team collaboration:** Team and project or program success depends upon *collaboration* — working together to achieve desired outcomes. This teamwork can be facilitated through effective and efficient communications such as the ability to share files while talking on the phone.

✔ **Controlling reachability:** Creating "one-number" access (where an individual has exactly one "phone" number for office, mobile, fax, and TTY) in order to speed up lookups and hookups.

✔ **Improving access to messages and calendar:** PIM (Personal Information Management, meaning your contacts, messages, and calendar) both frees workers and enslaves them. Improving access to information in PIMs, such as voice-access to calendars and messages, helps to improve your effectiveness by making it easier to reach key pieces of information quickly.

✔ **Creating the ability to reach experts:** Often you need to find not just people, but experts. How many times do we call one, two, or three people, trying to find the one person with the answer to a question? Why not build a directory — accessible to anyone who needs to know — of not only names, but also experts on key subjects? At other times you know who to go to for key content or contextual input and guidance, but you did not have the opportunity to ask, or the response came too late. UC makes anytime an opportunity to ask, and helps increase the probability that a response will be there when you need it.

✔ **Easing conference attendance:** Increase the intelligence and capabilities in conferencing systems, including: click-to-conference, improved media choices, and having a conference call you when it's time to begin.

All of these effectiveness success factors are facilitated by UC systems that are easy to use.

IT effectiveness

One of the great challenges in IT organizations today is the superfluity of technologies and systems they are required to support. Faced with financial challenges to do more with less, IT often assimilates too many systems, usually in small increments, resulting in a slow weakening of the IT organization in terms of its ability to adequately support everything. The entire organization suffers because of IT's lack of expertise and resources to support everything well.

Fully integrated solutions are far easier to support than solutions that are duct-taped together in-house. Some examples of the ways that IT organizations can become more effective include

- ✔ **Taking advantage of an agile technology environment:** The use of a service-oriented architecture (SOA) gives the IT environment greater agility and provides more opportunities for re-use.

- ✔ **Simplifying the technology environment:** Server consolidation, server virtualization, application consolidation, and moving to Web-based applications.

- ✔ **Working with standard applications and devices:** Using product and technology standards such as SIP means that IT can deploy more instances of technologies it already uses instead of adding one-offs.

These strategic moves can result in an IT department whose supported applications and environments are more reliable and secure, translating into greater confidence in IT from the rest of the organization (and outside of the organization as well, when it's highly collaborative with others).

Chapter 3

Establishing a Unified Communications Strategy

Deciding that UC is probably right for your organization is a relatively easy step. This chapter explores how you get from "I want UC" to a strategy that delivers just what you need for unifying your company communications. Any journey worth taking is worth planning, and at this stage you want to ponder the reach and depth of UC in your organization.

Whether you were smitten by the greater capabilities and promises of business effectiveness or lured by the prospects of lower costs, read on to discover how to realize UC in your organization.

Gaining Advantages with a Cohesive Strategy

The point of UC is not shiny new IP phones or SIP-aware instant messaging. Rather, UC is about integrating communications systems with each other and with customer-centric applications. A strategy for the introduction of UC into the enterprise needs to take these capabilities into account.

In order to create a viable strategy, it is helpful to know more about the distinguishing characteristics of Intelligent Communications, the big picture in which UC fits. If you understand the big picture, you can develop a strategy that will be more durable and viable for your organization.

Introducing Intelligent Communications

UC is a path to Intelligent Communications. At Avaya, Intelligent Communications is about embedding business communications applications into the very fabric of the business — into the business processes — to transform how the business serves its customers, how employees work on a daily basis, and how its various locations operate separately as well as together as a distributed enterprise.

Intelligent Communications is about making people more productive, customers more satisfied, and business processes more efficient. See Figure 3-1 for a visual of Intelligent Communications and the role that UC plays within it.

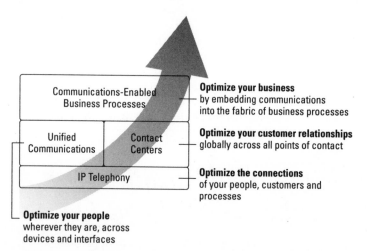

Figure 3-1: Unified Communications leads to Intelligent Communications.

Four core components enable Avaya to deliver Intelligent Communication solutions to its customers. These include:

- ✔ **IP Telephony.** This is the core underlying converged infrastructure (voice, video, and so on) that enables voice-grade performance with security, scale-ability, reliability, manage-ability and service-ability.

- ✔ **Unified Communications.** These solutions enable businesses to improve the productivity of their information workers by enabling them to be reachable and available anywhere, any time, via any of a wide array of devices and applications. Refer to Chapter 2 for more about the effectiveness of UC.

- ✔ **Contact Center.** These solutions enable businesses to achieve exceptional levels of customer satisfaction using any means that customers want to communicate — from speech access to self-service applications; e-mail, telephone, and so on. As you enhance the ability for customer contact, you bridge the contact center with the information worker in order to create "the enterprise ready to serve."

- ✔ **Communications-Enabled Business Processes.** These solutions enable communications to be integrated into the fabric of the business to allow orchestration of work in an efficient and effective manner.

As you think about IC and UC, think about your communications and customer-centric applications melding into one whole with two components: the traditional CRM (customer relationship management) part, and the communicating part — working together to improve customer communications and satisfaction.

Focusing on Costs

Okay, before you go soaring into your glorious future with Intelligent Communications, you probably need to get your feet back on the ground; time to make some coffee, sharpen your pencil, and figure out how you're going to pay for all of this. You may be surprised to discover that implementing UC need not be an expensive undertaking.

This isn't a book about accounting or corporate finance, so I simply stick to the principles that are essential to UC, which you can use as you develop your company's strategy. Here are some tips to help you keep costs under control:

- ✔ **You define the pace.** You can ease into UC or charge into UC — either way, proceed at a pace that is right for your organization. It is entirely up to you. Because UC is modular, you need only upgrade or replace the appropriate components as you go, in whatever order best meets your business objectives.

- ✔ **Remember support costs.** Don't forget to factor in periodic expenses such as technical support.

- ✔ **Consider multi-vendor integration.** Avaya's UC solutions work with all popular existing technologies (IBM Lotus: Domino, Notes, Sametime Instant Messaging and Web Conferencing; Microsoft: Exchange, Outlook, Live Communication Server, Office Communicator, Windows Mobile 5), so there is no need to wrest your desktop productivity applications out of the hands of your users and upgrade to something new. They can all get along under UC.

- ✔ **Determine big picture TCO.** When you are moving to a UC environment, you may be adding capabilities that your organization does not possess today. I mention this because some people fall into the trap of doing an apples-to-apples comparison, pitting old generation communication costs against UC costs, forgetting that UC is bringing a lot more *value*.

For a true apples to apples TCO, you need to estimate the cost of your less-effective communication today and put a dollar figure on it. For this you might make some estimates on revenue impact, or satisfaction rates and its impact on repeat business. Talk with people in Sales, Marketing, Services or Call Center Ops, Research & Development (or whatever your organization calls these) to get an idea of what those groups think the financial benefit of UC will be in your organization.

Focusing on Operational Issues

This section covers strategic challenges related to the day-to-day use of UC in an organization. This isn't a comprehensive list of issues to consider, but just a few of the important ones that you're likely to encounter. Even if all of these don't apply to your organization, preparing your company to address such issues can help you to discover which issues are important to you.

Aim for one-number-greets-all

One of the principle wins for UC is the integration of all telephone-number-centric technologies. Called *single-number access,* your Avaya provided communications gear can take in any sort of incoming communication: mobile, landline, voice-mail, fax, TTY, into a single phone number and sort it out automatically. That one number can be extended to any location be it in or around the office, a virtual office, home office, customer location, or hotel room. Think about how you would ideally want calls to route behind the scenes when a customer calls; Avaya can help make that happen and much more.

Supporting your users

Supporting your UC-enabled users is something you want to consider. Here are some principles to keep in mind:

- ✓ **Standard configurations.** Develop easily-supported standard configurations that will work for your users. For large or diverse user communities, you may need to develop multiple configuration profiles. Also, consider whether you can lock parts of the configuration so that users can't shoot themselves in the foot.

- ✓ **Event logging.** Make sure that your environment has a way of logging significant events from your users' equipment and programs, both as a sign of trouble but also for aid in troubleshooting.

- ✓ **Troubleshooting guides.** Make sure that your support staff is both trained on the new technologies they are supporting and also equipped with guides for figuring out common problems.

- ✓ **Replacement shipping.** Make sure that you have a way to get replacement equipment out to users in the fastest way possible, so that their downtime does not seriously affect their productivity. When you ship out replacement components, include ship-back tags and labels so that they can easily return defective equipment.

✔ **Software media.** Remote users who need to re-install software need to have local copies of media that they can reload from, so that they don't have to wait for shipped CDs or wait for time-consuming downloads.

With new capabilities in the hands of your users, your support capabilities need to stay in step with them.

Creating accessibility policies

You need to develop your worker-application and worker-communication use cases so that you have an idea of all of the common scenarios that you will need to support.

With UC, you *can* provide access for many applications and functions from many device type, but does that mean you *should*? You may determine that some functions should only be accessed through a firewall-protected laptop but not from a lighter mobile device such as a smartphone. Accessibility policies represent both the capabilities that you want to make available, as well as the permissions for performing functions or accessing information. This goes for devices within the enterprise network, as well as devices that remote employees use.

The process of creating accessibility policies can also be a means for reducing the types of access you deliver. Project teams can only do so much in a given period of time; scaling back from *all-possible-scenarios* to those that are most likely to be needed and used may be a good way of managing implementation resources and schedules.

Ensuring security behind — and beyond — the firewall

Get your organization's security analysts involved in your UC strategy from the get-go. They are likely aware of issues that may influence how you design or deploy your future UC environment. For instance, you might not want your CFO to be able to approve large purchases using his or her smartphone's browser, because of the differences in Sarbanes-Oxley-required access controls available for smartphones. Being unaware of such issues could cause the project to stumble later, causing you to go back to the whiteboard.

Adding UC capabilities in the enterprise also means making changes within the enterprise network. Doing so can accommodate the new network traffic and patterns you must expect when introducing VoIP and SIP, for instance.

But more than that, remember that your remote workers are away from the protection of your enterprise firewalls and other controls. Hardware and software solutions that your remote workers can use may require protection that may not be a part of the solutions that you're putting into their hands. Competent security analysts will recognize the risks associated with your new technologies — engage them early and often in order to keep risks in your organization low.

Focusing on Business Outcomes

Keeping your eye on business outcomes is the most vital task when building your UC strategy. Like any business decision that is related to a strategic initiative, the support of business goals and objectives must be the desired outcome.

Going a little deeper, specific themes that you can focus on are

- ✓ **Value.** Your UC strategy needs to unlock value in your organization in the form of improved customer interactions and satisfaction, worker productivity, accelerated work flow and business process flow, and reduced support costs.

- ✓ **Risk protection.** You want to chart your organization in a direction that will protect you from the need to make costly and/or disruptive changes to communications in the future. You need to choose durable standards and able organizations like Avaya.

- ✓ **Employee retention.** Your employees *are* your organization. As tenure increases, so does knowledge about your products, services, customers, and culture. Employees who are able to easily and successfully communicate are more apt to be satisfied employees who will stay with you for the long haul.

These outcomes will be more specific in your own organization, as you introduce or expand UC to address specific business objectives — your pain points or your growth opportunities.

Improving customer interactions

One of the top objectives in most organizations is customer satisfaction. Achieving high customer satisfaction is done in two ways: high-quality products and services, and exceptional customer service when your customers want or need to interact with you. Consider how UC contributes to improved customer interaction.

Simplifying interactions with customers

You can implement a single number for customers to access an associate for a variety of services, be it voice, fax, notification, or TTY. This number can stay the same regardless of the owner's location, be it at their office desk, around the office, on their mobile device, virtual or work-at-home office, or on their PC from anywhere in the world. Single number access works for both inbound as well as outbound calls. Incoming calls to the worker's (or department's) one number can always be directed to the right phone, regardless of location. Similarly, outbound calls reflect the worker's single-number caller ID regardless of where a call actually originates.

Also, workers can transfer calls to, or include in an ad-hoc conference call, another coworker through her single number — regardless of her actual location or device she's using at the time.

Increasing availability of associates

Simultaneous ringing of business lines and cell phones coupled with "find-me" or "follow-me" services increase the probability that a caller can reach the intended person on the first attempt. Customers who can easily reach the right person are less apt to begin focusing on the difficulty of getting help instead of the issue they needed help with in the first place.

Increasing responsiveness

Customers and employees can reach the right persons, and also initiate real-time and non-real-time communications from anywhere. Employees can have increased access to other associates to deal with customer or vendor issues. All business voice messages are managed in a single mailbox, eliminating the challenge of forwarding important messages that are left in a mailbox associated with a cell phone or alternate location to another associate for information or action. Improved notification of (and access to) messages (e-mail, voicemail, fax), and increased ability to manage those messages accelerates the company's ability to deal with customer demands.

Increasing productivity

UC frees up time otherwise wasted on outdated communications systems trying to find people. The benefits of improved productivity are myriad. This section describes just a few.

Speeding up execution

Employees have improved and have faster access to other associates. They can more easily reach external customers, suppliers, partners, and stakeholders to address issues, create opportunities, and advance work flow.

Keeping tabs on consumer spending limits

UC in the financial industry can aid customer relations. Today, most banks don't have a way of informing a customer when they are nearing their credit or debit card spending limits. This situation can result in customer embarrassment and the customer associating that negative experience with that bank's spending card.

Banks can improve customer loyalty by using Unified Communications to keep their customers informed about the status of transactions and spending limits via outbound voice calls or messages. In fact, instead of merely informing customers of impending limits, the communication can be interactive, providing the customer with the ability to review recent transactions or even make back-end transactions such as transfers and draws, thereby enabling transactions, improving the customer experience, and assuring brand loyalty.

Hitching up with unified roadside assistance

UC helps service companies better the people who need their help. For example, even with today's reliable vehicles, people still find themselves stranded by the side of the road with a variety of situations including flat tires, broken parts, no fuel, and accidents. The challenge for the roadside assistance center is to deliver the most timely response to customers by using field-based resources in the most efficient manner possible.

Incoming calls for roadside assistance reach a contact center, which dispatches the appropriate aid, as well as a rough estimate on the time to service delivery. Motorists' experiences are frequently negative, based upon inaccurate expectations and insufficient communications.

Unified communications can improve customer service and management of field based resources, by providing:

✔ Real time voice and/or text messaging between dispatch, field resources, and the motorist.

✔ Location and resource based scheduling that improves dispatch efficiency and gets the right resources to the motorist.

The results of improved communications capabilities include more satisfied motorists that results in brand loyalty, more efficient use of resources that results in reduced costs.

Improving effectiveness and efficiency

Increasing the ability for people to communicate with each other increases their ability to do the right thing and do things right. Providing communication tools across formerly separate device- and network-appropriate environments transforms wasted time into productive time. Simplified communication interfaces increase the user adoption rate of communication tools, resulting in workers taking advantage of productivity tools that were previously too complex to use beyond the "power users."

Integrating communications

Integrated communications reduces the need to manage multiple devices or synchronize information among environments.

With increased control of conferencing tools, employees are empowered to spend more time on the purpose of virtual meetings, and less time managing conferencing resources and technology or dealing with interruptions such as noisy lines caused by music on hold, cell phones, and noisy backgrounds. The ability to manage and control one's inbound and outbound communications increases an employee's ability to focus on what matters, rather than focusing on the technology itself.

Providing content and context

Improved access to people and messages provides necessary information to assist in decision making and workflow — often in a just-in-time manner. The ability to see associates through video interfaces as well as hearing their voices while participating in conference calls or listening to voice messages adds important context to the information at hand.

Enhancing collaboration

Collaboration is the ability for different groups and teams to work together to achieve business goals. UC improves collaboration in several ways that are described here.

Simplifying work flow

The integration of directories and presence information into communication tools increases the ability to access others — and in the most appropriate means. This accelerates access to decision makers, content and process experts, team members and employee groups, and external customers, suppliers, partners, and stakeholders. Simplified communication tools increases the frequency (volume) and intensity (quality, richness) of Communication — empowering people with greater knowledge and context to communicate and get things done.

Decision making the smart way

Employees can access decision makers in a more timely fashion and consult more with others to gather necessary content and contextual information leading to faster and better decisions. They can then share those decisions with individuals, groups, or the entire enterprise to keep individuals and teams up to date.

Social networking

UC can increase the ability and propensity to collaborate. This trend leads to better team relationships which improves project and program outcomes.

Reducing costs and risks

A sound UC strategy results in reduced costs, freeing up capital for other critical initiatives. Risks of future disruptions are reduced, allowing company executive and managers to focus on production and services. The outcomes you can anticipate are discussed here.

Saving on collaborative and mobile expenses

In-house audio and Web conferencing facilities can significantly reduce collaboration expenses associated with service providers — often resulting in a return on investment in under a year. You've probably noticed this phenomenon around your own company: Cell phones are used a lot from the office, essentially wasting minutes from expensive cell phone plans. The ability to answer a call on a cell phone and shift it to a desk phone can reduce cell phone minutes for when they are truly needed.

The use of a single personal directory available to all communication tools reduces the use of device-dependent directories and device usage when less expensive means are available. Directories can include access to not only the people you regularly work with, but also experts in various subjects important in the organization, and the entire enterprise directory.

Dual mode phones enable associates to use a single mobile device to access public cell phone services while away from the office, and seamlessly switch to private WiFi facilities while in and around the office or campus environment.

Customer control and retention

UC can increase customer loyalty by simplifying interactions with customers, increasing the availability of employees, and accelerating the responsiveness to their needs.

Linking locations for enhanced emergency service

With seven phone systems installed in five different buildings, Strafford County of New Hampshire faced a daunting challenge when local phone company lines into those buildings began to deteriorate and a complete system upgrade was needed. The situation looked desperate. "We needed to install a system that would allow for growth and offered features that would allow us to reduce expenses and provide better services to county citizens," said Roger Smith, information management systems director and chief information office.

Strafford County needed to improve 911 service, enhance the public image, and provide better services. The county also needed better phone support to meet its disaster recovery needs.

The project team developed requirements and specifications, and ultimately was most impressed with Avaya's proposal.

Avaya's business partner installed new cabling, switches, servers, and phones throughout the county offices. Avaya Extension to Cellular was also deployed, keeping field-based county employees in touch with central offices. The result: vastly increased services, new functionality (including intra-state video-conferencing), integration with the statewide court system application, and greater reliability — all with no increase in budget.

Single number access means that whenever a customer calls someone at the enterprise, they are simply calling a business number associated with the enterprise. This single number eliminates the need for customers to call cell phone numbers, which creates the risk of losing the customer contact should the employee leave the enterprise and take that cell phone number with him.

Opportunity costs

Increasing employee productivity increases the leverage of the overall workforce. Simplifying the act of communicating, and integrating it into what people do, ensures that communications take place when and how they should. This eliminates the cost of unsuccessful communications — those not made or delayed because it was inconvenient, or because the ability to do so was not readably available.

In the event of a business interruption — be it disasters related to a health epidemic or pandemic, weather (snow storms, hurricanes), transportation and utility outages, terrorist alerts, labor unrest, or a dry run for disaster preparedness — it is critical that people can continue to communicate.

UC capabilities allow people to work and communicate from anywhere. Avaya Unified Communications solutions are based on open standards and are designed to interwork with a large ecosystem of vendors, business applications, and devices. This flexibility allows a customer to integrate communication applications today to take advantage of the immediate benefits; knowing that if their topology changes in the future due to strategic changes, acquisitions, or the availability of new solutions that their UC services will be able to adapt.

Building Your Own Business Case

Are you ready to get started and figure out how UC can work in your organization? As you build your strategy and your business case, step back and take the time to understand some key characteristics about your organization.

Understanding your workforce

Consider the types of workers you have, what they do, and where they do it:

- What percentage of your workforce performs administrative roles?
  - Are these workers primarily desk-bound, or do they roam throughout buildings or campuses?
  - Do they require access to directories and calendars?
  - Do they require access to IT applications (e.g. insurance, scheduling, or billing)?
- What percentage of your workforce performs sales or other professional roles?
  - What priority is placed on these workers for customer response and satisfaction?

> - Do these workers travel extensively?
>
> - Do these workers require access to information (such as offer and pricing) while mobile?
>
> - Do these workers require access to ordering applications?
>
> - Do these workers use a variety of devices that have multiple form factors and interfaces?
>
> ✔ What percentage of your workforce performs IT and technical roles?
>
>> - To what extent do these workers need to collaborate within technical teams and with users and constituents?
>>
>> - To what extent must these workers be available to resolve technical issues?
>>
>> - To what extent do these workers require remote access to systems and management tools?

Answering these questions can help you begin to see what contexts and functions are required by your workforce.

Understanding your technical environment

It is also helpful for you to know what technology is being used in your organization today and what initiatives for updating that technology are currently underway. UC can integrate with and/or replace technologies you currently use. Some examples include:

> ✔ Voicemail upgrades
>
> ✔ Mobile users with PIM or application connectivity
>
> ✔ Enterprise Instant Messaging
>
> ✔ Microsoft environments: Exchange/Outlook, Office Communicator/Live Communication Server
>
> ✔ IBM environments: Domino/Notes, Sametime
>
> ✔ Service providers for audio or Web conferencing

Understanding your objectives

You need to understand where your company's business priorities are today and in the near-term. One or more of the following may be important in your organization:

- ✔ Becoming more customer-focused
- ✔ Increasing business agility
- ✔ Addressing productivity at the enterprise (versus task) level, such as revenue or profit per employee
- ✔ Improving operational efficiency
- ✔ Increasing leverage from the employee base
- ✔ Reducing communication expense
- ✔ Reducing business risk

It helps to be aware of the enterprise big picture. UC is a big-picture environment that touches everything, not a niche solution that fits in between existing components.

For example, suppose your company is planning an instant messaging system upgrade. You can begin executing a UC strategy by starting with messaging unification. In one enterprise, the IT department created a simple desktop banner with caller ID and click-to-call features integrated to their corporate directory — all powered by Avaya Communication Manager. By keeping your broader UC strategy in mind at this early stage, you're well on your way to attaining the benefits that a unified solution can deliver.

Armed with the information in this section, you can build a business case that provides a better big-picture, strategic fit to help propel your business forward into UC.

Chapter 4

Evolving into Intelligent Communications

*W*ondrous as UC may seem, it is not your ultimate destination. Instead, like the communications capabilities you and your organization had in the past, UC is a stepping stone to the *next* communications stage. As your company grows, matures, and adopts UC, it is evolving into the future of Intelligent Communications.

Establishing and refining communications is a journey. Technology advances; business needs change; customer expectations grow. Communication is the key to this growth: effective communications give your business a better *now*, and pave the way for an even better future.

I outline the journey in this chapter. Find where your organization is, and put on your *vision cap* to see where you're going next.

 Riding the wave of communications evolution is not about throwing the old stuff away and getting new stuff. Rather, it's about accumulating and refining business capabilities through communications. Each step *builds* on the previous one.

Basic Communications

The world that I call *basic communications* is an environment that consists of an assortment of communications capabilities in the organization, many of which are legacy applications. At this stage, the main business driver is containing cost and the main way you measure success is in cost savings.

The primary thing to notice is that all of these communications capabilities are, primarily, unrelated to one another. Each exists as a standalone capability with no awareness of, or connections to, others. In many cases, they use different infrastructure, devices, and directory information. Often the technologies are unrelated — but even when the same technologies are present (such as a desk phone and a mobile phone), they are often still separate from one another (separate access numbers and voice mail). Basic communications use disparate tools such as:

- **Telephony.** This is basic voice communications. You may have analog phones, digital phones, as well as wireless phones from the wireless telecommunications services. Every phone has its own number and functions more or less without awareness of the others (unless you happen to leave a voice message on one phone telling the caller to try your other number).

- **Call coverage and notification.** This is a scant capability in basic communications. Manually transferring calls from one mode to another is often not possible. Forwarding office extensions can only be done from that office phone, so call-forwarding features must be programmed manually before you leave

- **Voice-mail.** Characteristic of basic voice-mail is that voice-mail boxes for office, mobile and remote office numbers are separate islands; notifications for each are also separate. Because workers often don't know when they have messages waiting for them, they must repeatedly call their disparate voice-mail boxes to see whether messages are waiting. And messages in one voice-mail system cannot be transferred to other voice-mail systems.

✔ **Messaging:** Workers have many modes of text communications available — e-mail, Instant Messaging (IM), and mobile text-to-text messaging — all of which are separate from and unaware of one another. Each of these modes also has a separate user interface that users have to learn, making for a more complex user experience.

✔ **Conferencing.** The capabilities of bringing multiple parties together for voice-communications are varied and separate. All require manual, proactive effort.

✔ **Directories.** Perhaps the most visible characteristic of basic communications is the multitude of isolated directories that exist for each of the separate services. In most cases, you can't transfer directory information from one medium to another (doing so manually doesn't count). Non-native contact information (for instance, a mobile number in an e-mail directory) is often outdated or missing altogether.

✔ **Availability.** With few exceptions, it's impossible to tell which communications modes a person is using at the time, which makes the effort to raise a conversation an exercise in futility. Try the desk number, the mobile number, the home office number, IM, fax, e-mail. How many attempts does it take to figure out that the recipient is on an airplane or out of coverage? Answer: after *all* of the attempts, you *still* don't know whether the recipient is truly away or just in an important meeting for another 15 minutes.

Many companies are still coping with basic communications today. And it can be a truly frustrating, inefficient experience.

Converged Communications

In the world of converged communications, the various mediums of communications begin to have threads of connectivity to and awareness of other mediums. These threads may be thin, custom *integrations* or gateways that provide limited capabilities. The business driver at this stage is improved productivity and companies typically measure success in terms of productivity enhancements and infrastructure consolidation.

Converged communications tools include:

- **Telephony:** VoIP communications provides voice connectivity capabilities on a wider range of devices (soft phones, SIP phones, PDAs) and network technologies (LAN, WAN, WiFi, broadband wireless), bringing what is probably the most important mode of communications, *talking real-time,* to more workers in more situations.

- **Contact:** It becomes easier to reach individuals at the office when there is only one number to call for voice, fax, or TTY, through advances in the office PBX. However, workers still have separate pager and wireless numbers. Convergence is limited, but present in some forms.

- **Call coverage and notification:** Capabilities emerge that handle incoming calls a little bit faster, with limited awareness of other mediums. Call transfers between mediums and messaging alerts in out-of-band mediums emerge (for instance, a text or e-mail message alerting you to the presence of new office voice-mail messages).

- **Messaging:** Some media integration occurs: e-mail to mobile devices, a wider array of voice-mail notifications across other media, gateways to instant messaging. These are almost likely point solutions created to deal with some of the isolation of all of these means for communications.

- **Conferencing:** Improved audio conferencing capabilities: the conference calls the callers (and not the other way around), integrated Web and video conferencing, outsourced or in-house conferencing.

- **Directories:** Various mediums begin to use common, centralized directories such as LDAP. Directories have limited synchronization capabilities with one another, resulting in more complete and accurate directory information.

- **Availability:** Various communications provide limited information on the availability and presence of others: IM shows when buddies are available, away, or off the air. Calendars become more network-enabled to allow workers to see when others are unavailable (and why), RFID and GPS provide location information in some cases.

Converged communications is the beginning of bridging the many separate communication mediums, by providing some limited gateway-like functions, thin bridges between these separate islands.

Unified Communications

UC is the stage of the journey that this book is all about, and the path many companies are taking to enable interaction across a virtual enterprise. The measures of success include both accelerated workflow, regardless of where employees are working from, and improved customer loyalty. The characteristics of UC are described here and referenced throughout this book:

- ✔ **Telephony:** Voice communications take place over UC clients, which take the form of thick or thin clients, SIP phones, and dual-mode wireless phones that can communicate with telecommunications networks over GSM or CDMA and within the enterprise over WiFi.

- ✔ **Contact:** Workers have true single-number access: call one number and you find them, regardless of their mode of communications available at that moment. All outbound communications likewise have a single-number origination.

- ✔ **Call coverage and notification:** Rules and filters determine how and where incoming calls should be routed, based upon caller identity, time of day, and current business conditions. Message waiting indicator (MWI) is intelligent and provides more value than a blinking light or symbol.

- ✔ **Messaging:** Workers have single voice-mail, e-mail to any device, cross-media reply and forwarding, and federated text and instant messaging.

- ✔ **Conferencing:** Audio, video, and Web conferencing calls the participants on whatever means they have available; they also integrate into calendars and PIMs, and provide telepresence.

- ✔ **Directories:** Directories are integrated into all communications types and provide click-to-call (or text or message) capability.

- ✔ **Availability:** Integrated or federated presence shows which modes are available for recipients. Workers can edit their preference profiles.

Chapter 2 provides more complete and concise descriptions of all of these capabilities. Discussion on developing a strategy and business outcomes with UC is found in Chapter 3.

Intelligent Communications

As your communications evolution advances and matures, your company can move from UC to Intelligent Communications, known as IC. It's more important to understand *why* IC than what makes it work. The business drivers and objectives that come into play are:

- ✔ **Improved customer satisfaction:** Whether you rely on inbound or outbound calling, phone or Web-based self-service, or all of these, you want your customers to be able to manage their service and get help fast.

- ✔ **Reduced costs:** Facing or creating competitive pressures, you want to streamline and automate processes, make information available faster, reduce the probability that problems will occur, and solve them faster.

- ✔ **Communications-Enabled Business Processes (CEBP):** Traditional and emerging business processes associated with implementation, service, and support — as well as other customer-facing processes, can be communications-enabled. This means embedding communications capabilities such as messaging, telephony, conferencing, availability, and presence right into processes instead of external capabilities that support them. This results in processes that are instantly aware of the availability of experts and support personnel, and can facilitate real-time communications with these persons in order to keep things moving on time and within everyone's expectations.

These business objectives drive the development and implementation of specific business-enabling capabilities, which I discuss in the following sections.

Orchestrated communications

IC-enabled applications and conferences can orchestrate communications based upon available preferences and needs. Instead of participants needing to look up conference codes and URLs in calendaring systems, conferences call participants at the appointed time by whatever means they have available at the moment. Applications provide needed business information for status or decision-making proactively, instead of waiting for the customer or decision maker to call and check on status.

VIP routing

Intelligent Communications are generally thought of as sender- and recipient-agnostic, driven by simple rules that don't take into account an often overlooked fact: the specific identity of the originator (caller or sender) or recipient. VIP routing adds a dimension of call routing ability by speeding communications to and from important senders and recipients, regardless of specific preferences. It's the digital form of "put that call through *now!*"

Personal assistant

An automated assistant, available by whatever means are available at the moment (speech, text, Web) can help a worker find specific information, a subject matter expert, or a specific individual. Business rules guide the inquiry and subsequent communications to the best available resource in the least amount of time.

Particularly helpful during "windshield time," a virtual personal assistant that is always on can help you stay connected, prioritize, and respond quickly. Your assistant might ask, "*You have a call from your favorite client, would you like to accept this call?*" or remind you, "*You have an upcoming meeting.*" If you enable hands-free, eyes-free speech access to your assistant, you can speak commands such as, "*Read my messages,*" "*Find free time tomorrow,*" or "*Conference all lines*" — thereby gaining back valuable time that would otherwise be lost.

Threshold-driven alerts/ notifications

IC provides the alerts found in converged communications and UC, but with greater intelligence and value. For instance, unanswered voicemail can result in escalations to peers or managers. Aging emails from customers can generate "you have waiting questions!" calls to one's mobile phone. Undelivered text or IM messages can be routed via e-mail or text-to-speech calls to one's phone.

IC brings unanswered messages to the next level that are business process centric rather than just recipient-centric. It's about the process and the customer, not the vacationing or too-busy recipient.

CEBP-driven interactions

Communications-enabled business processes, or *CEBP,* is what IC is all about. Business processes are combinations of both data systems and human action. As people go about their jobs, they rely upon communication with other workers, customers, suppliers, partners, and so on. But business process stops when the next step is waiting on human response and action. With human latency introduced, your business process is vulnerable to error as well as delay.

By embedding communications capabilities directly into business process workflow and supporting applications, business processes can move more swiftly because of the more efficient execution of the human actions in the process, rather than just sit on the sideline and wait for an action that relies on an impending communication. Each business has unique business processes that can be improved by Intelligent Communications. Consider some examples of CEBP interactions.

- ✔ **Insurance Company:** Roadside assistance finds the right tow truck or repair person, any necessary parts, while keeping the customer informed.

- ✔ **Banking Institution:** Retail banks can create value-add services such as proactively notifying credit card customers who are reaching spending limits. Instead of denying the next credit card transaction, the customer's bank can proactively engage the customer in a two-way communication, which not only informs the customer of the spending threshold, but also affords them the ability to transfer funds or review recent transactions. Capital markets firms can leverage CEBP and improve back-office/middle-office workflows by automating the communications required to handle and close exception situations in areas such as trade processing.

✓ **Manufacturing Company:** Manufacturers can improve production line management as soon as they identify contamination or quality problems because they can automatically notify the line management and supporting team members and bring them together to resolve the problem more quickly.

✓ **Airline Company:** Intelligent travel fulfillment means that rather than suffer the angst of one overbooked flight followed by undersold flights, an airline can proactively notify travelers based upon their preferences, by offering them alternatives. This gives travelers more choices while giving the airline more opportunities to fill flights to capacity with passengers who are on the flights they wanted (which may not be the flights they purchased).

✓ **Medical Office:** When scheduling patients, last-minute changes in provider and facilities availability often result in bumped appointments and procedures. By keeping providers and patients informed of bottlenecks and shortages, both are able to rearrange their schedules based upon their needs.

These are just a few examples of the ways that CEBP can impact business productivity and customer loyalty, and there are many more. Think about which processes in your own company could be communications-enabled and how your company could benefit from faster response time, access to experts, rich collaboration, and improved customer interactions.

Chapter 5

Eight Tips for Implementing Unified Communications

In This Chapter

▶ Create your worker profiles

▶ Make the most of what you've already got

▶ Use proven technologies to simplify and save money

▶ Ask questions and embrace change

*Y*ou already know how the story is going to end for you: with a Unified Communications strategy that you'll soon implement to create better outcomes. The tips in this chapter are designed to nudge you in the right direction in order to ensure success with your strategy. You and your business deserve it!

Create a Worker Snapshot

Before you can propose possibly-sweeping changes in the way that your organization communicates today, you need to understand how your employees communicate with the tools that they have right now.

This is especially vital in companies with multiple locations, highly mobile workers, and consistent outsourcing of certain functions. Here's a rundown of the situations you need to consider:

✔ People who work at their desk and have access to a computer all day

✔ People who have little or no computer access

- Branch offices
- Virtual workers, such as those who work out of their homes and other "off-campus" locations
- On-the-go salespeople
- Workers with long commutes
- Outsourced business partners and vendors, especially where you need frequent and secure communications
- Mergers and acquisitions, which may involve different parts of your organization with different communications technologies and styles
- Multinational locations, where different time zones, customs and regulations may have an impact on communications

After you've identified all of these "internal" communication needs and patterns, chart them in terms of their business functions, technologies in use, and other factors that are relevant, such as urgency and frequency of communications. This chart can function as your baseline for worker communications — you'll need it when you build your business case.

Focus on Your Client

Remember when strategizing that the customer is always right. With the return to emphasis on customer service, make sure that your Unified Communications strategy retains or improves your customers' ability to reach your workers easily. In concept this has always been a no-brainer, but with your workers scattered throughout multiple locations and time zones, communication still needs to be seamless and easy for your clients.

Advances in communications technology from Avaya have made it possible for organizations like yours to make client communications experiences better than ever before, even when taking into account that all of your workers are no longer necessarily situated in one corporate locale. Whether clients need customer service or the inside scoop from an out-today-but-reachable-by-IM expert, you can make them feel "at home" as soon as they enter your company's communications channels by making phone tag, guess my cell phone number, and similar waiting games a thing of the past.

Leverage Existing Infrastructures and Applications

Your communications strategy should, to the greatest extent possible, leverage what you already have in place. Today's communications infrastructures are modular, and often permit logical overlays of multiple services. VLANs (virtual local area networks) permit voice and data networks to occupy the same physical network wiring, for instance.

Similarly, you may be able to use your existing Internet connections to carry some or all of your VoIP traffic to and from your branch offices and/or your telco providers. You really don't need to overhaul your entire network, hardware, and software to get make great strides toward Unified Communications; Avaya can help you see where you can migrate, transform, and evolve your current setup over time.

Additionally, you may be able to make your existing applications communications-aware, such as e-mail and instant messaging. This step both saves cost (by necessitating less training) and improves productivity.

Converge Networks

As you develop your long-term communications strategy, you need to seriously consider converging your voice and data networks. Convergence is a key step on your UC journey. A few ways you can do this include

- ✔ **Single wiring plant:** Although your existing building may have duplicate voice and data network wiring plants, you can save money in future buildings by building a single data network wiring plant for both voice and data.

- ✔ **Single backbone:** When you make the switch to IP Telephony (VoIP), you can rely upon a single network backbone to carry your enterprise data and voice traffic.

> ✔ **Single Internet connection:** You can realize potentially significant savings by converging your voice and data Internet connections into a single data connection to carry your voice and data. Your voice connections to the outside world can travel through H.323 or SIP trunks right in your data connection to your IP telephony network provider. Won't it feel good to cut the voice trunk cord!?

Take Advantage of Proven Technologies

Voice and data communications technologies are mature and proven. Resist the temptation, no matter how powerful, to risk your business on untested or proprietary technologies. You don't want to end up with the Betamax of communications technologies — in other words, obsolescence and the prospect of a costly migration in the future.

Some questions you can ask of your communications vendors include:

> ✔ How long has your technology been in the field?
>
> ✔ How many organizations have implemented — and are still using — your technologies?
>
> ✔ Are your technologies based on open standards?
>
> ✔ Do your products interoperate with those from other vendors?

Pay attention to the vendors' answers, and *how* they answer these tough questions. If they get all squirmy and uncomfortable, or brush off answering specifics with a cocky "we work with everything!" attitude, it may be time to walk away.

Implement Powerful Management Tools

While developing your communications strategy, be sure to include the management tools you need to operate within the environment smoothly. The capabilities that you need include:

✔ **Troubleshooting:** You need tools that help you to quickly identify faults, performance, and capacity issues. You may need to implement new troubleshooting processes to test solutions across all your communications channels in the fluid, mobile real world, not just inside the secure firewalls of the corporate network. And you need to provide a way for virtual users to access IT help remotely and train troubleshooting IT employees in how to help remote workers.

✔ **Reporting:** The old phrase "if you can't measure it, you can't manage it" applies here. Unless you can readily see how your UC network is being used, it is difficult to make decisions about the future or understand the present. Besides, you want to show off to the execs how much more efficiently your Unified Communications strategy is using resources than the old cobbled-together solution did.

Management tools like these will help you to unleash the power of your unified communications strategy.

Seek Expert Help

Chances are you're an expert in your business, which is probably not UC. Don't be afraid to seek help. You're reading this book, and that's a pretty good indicator that you want to find out more. When considering solutions providers, ask them the tough questions. If they are truly experienced, they should be able to answer your questions.

Outside consultants can also provide valuable guidance. An experienced consultant can often help identify business and technology issues that may have gone undiscovered until later.

Avaya Global Services, the world-wide full service organization, can help you "explore the possibilities," help you develop your plans, and even implement your UC solution. To find out more about how Avaya Global Services can enhance your customer service, employee productivity, and operational effectiveness by fully leveraging Intelligent Communications, contact your Avaya Business Partner or visit Avaya at www.avaya.com.

Don't Be Afraid of Change

By human nature, you're likely to get apprehensive when it comes to change, even when you're in control. And when we aren't in control, then changes can be downright scary.

When you start to get involved in Unified Communications, you're involved with systematic changes that can help your organization be more effective at what it does best. Even though the changes may be disruptive at first, the best way to deal with changes is to anticipate them and talk through the changes with stakeholders, in order to uncover additional issues. This will help to avoid surprises — the kinds of changes that are no fun.

Change can also be exciting, when you keep in mind the benefits that your business will realize as you adopt your unified communications strategy.

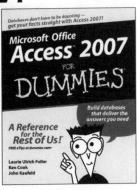

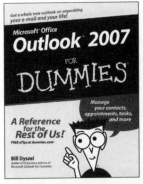

I'm Jorge.

I'M VP OF OPERATIONS.
I'M FLYING SOLO.
BUT I'VE GOT MY ENTIRE
BACK-UP TEAM ON
CONFERENCE EVERY
TIME I PRESS "ON"

SEE HOW INTELLIGENT COMMUNICATIONS
IS CHANGING JORGE'S WORLD AT AVAYA.COM

AVAYA
INTELLIGENT COMMUNICATIONS